CLASSIC LANDFORMS OF THE

GOWER
COAST

View at Bay

CLASSIC LANDFORMS OF THE

GOWER
COAST

EM BRIDGES

**Formerly University of Wales, Swansea and
International Soil Reference and Information Centre
in The Netherlands**

Series editors
Rodney Castleden and Christopher Green

Published by the Geographical Association
in conjunction with the
British Geomorphological Research Group

THE GEOGRAPHICAL ASSOCIATION

THE BRITISH GEOMORPHOLOGICAL RESEARCH GROUP

PREFACE

Geomorphologists study landforms and the processes that create and modify them. The results of their work, published as they invariably are in specialist journals, usually remain inaccessible to the general public. We would like to put that right. Scattered across the landscapes of England and Wales there are many beautiful and striking landforms that delight the eye of the general public and are also visited by educational parties from schools, colleges and universities. Our aim in producing this series of guides is to make modern explanations of these classic landforms available to all, in a style and format that will be easy to use in the field. We hope that an informed understanding of the origins of the features will help the visitor to enjoy the landscape all the more.

Encouraged by the success of the first edition of the Classic Landform Guides we are pleased to introduce this new edition, enhanced by colour photographs, new illustrations and with the valuable addition of 1:50 000 map extracts by kind permission of the Education Team, Ordnance Survey. The relevant map for the area covered in this booklet is the Ordnance Survey 1:50 000 Landranger sheet 159. Please refer to the current Ordnance Survey Index for 1:25 000 availability.

Rodney Castleden *Roedean School, Brighton*
Christopher Green *Royal Holloway, University of London*

ISBN 1 899085 50 5
This edition first published 1997
Published by the Geographical Association, 160 Solly Street, Sheffield S1 4BF.
The views expressed in this publication are those of the author and do not necessarily
represent those of the Geographical Association.
The Geographical Association is a registered charity no. 313129.

CONTENTS

Introduction	*6*
The Limestone Cliffs of Gower	*13*
Mumbles and Langland Bay	*16*
Pwlldu Head to Threecliff Bay	*18*
Oxwich Point to Rhossili	*27*
The Sandy Shores of Gower	*32*
Llanrhidian Marsh	*42*
Cefn Bryn	*45*
Glossary	*47*
Bibliography	*48*

Help and advice

Seasonal restrictions on visits to the National Nature Reserves are imposed when birds are nesting. Individual access is normally without restriction but visiting groups should seek advice. The relevant authorities for the area covered by this guide are: The Countryside Council for Wales, RVB House, Llysfelin Newydd, Phoenix Way, Enterprise Park, Llansamlet, Swansea SA7 9FG (Tel: 01792 771949), and The National Trust Warden for Gower, Reynoldston, Swansea (Tel: 01792 390636).

Cover photograph: Threecliff Bay. Photo: Mark Button.
Frontispiece: Raised beach and Fossil Cliffs, Mewslade Bay. Photo: Mark Button.
Acknowledgements
The author wishes to thank Dr R.A. Shakesby of University of Wales, Swansea for reading and making constructive comments upon the manuscript of this book.
The Geographical Association would like to thank the following organisations for permission to reproduce material in this publication: Mark Button Landscape Photography, Gower. Mapping reproduced from Ordnance Survey 1:50 000 Landranger mapping with the permission of The Controller of Her Majesty's Stationary Office
© Crown Copyright 82324M 09/96
Edited by: Rose Pipes
Illustrations: Paul Coles
Series design concept: Quarto Design, Huddersfield
Design and typesetting: Armitage Typo/Graphics, Huddersfield
Printed and bound in Hong Kong by: Colorcraft Limited

INTRODUCTION

The Gower Peninsula is one of the best known and most attractive parts of the coast of South Wales and was the first area in Britain to be designated as an Area of Outstanding Natural Beauty. Lying between Swansea and Carmarthen Bays, it extends 20km westwards from the city of Swansea and is bounded to the south by magnificent limestone cliffs with sandy bays and to the north by the extensive marshes of the Burry Estuary. The southern coast includes, in addition to the limestone cliffs, **raised beaches**, fossiliferous caves and their associated glacial and solifluction deposits. In places blown sand covers the solid rocks, as at Pennard (SS 566888), whereas at Whiteford Point the dune complex overlies shingle derived from glacial debris. In its lee alluvial silts accumulated to form Llanrhidian Marsh on the northern side of the peninsula (Figure 1).

The geological background

The oldest rocks to crop out in the Gower Peninsula are the sandstones and conglomerates of the Devonian Old Red Sandstone which form low rounded hills rising to 180m (Figure 2). These Devonian rocks appear in the cores of anticlines, the axes of which trend in a west-north-west to east-south-east direction (Figure 3) (George, 1940). Surrounding these low hills, the Carboniferous

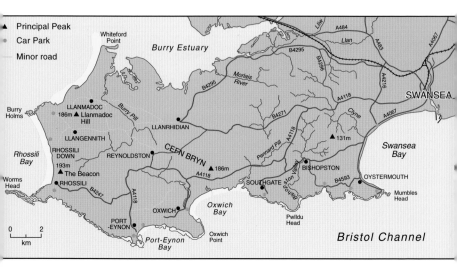

Figure 1: The Gower Peninsula: location and access.

Limestone forms a plateau at about 60m above sea-level, ending abruptly in the cliffs of the south coast. Both the Old Red Sandstone and Carboniferous rocks are tightly folded; if they could be straightened out, the width of the peninsula would be almost doubled! North-east of a line between Llanrhidian and Oystermouth the Carboniferous Limestone is succeeded by the Namurian Millstone Grit (Figure 3), here represented by shales, and the Coal Measures which form a scarp and vale landscape extending across the neck of the peninsula between Swansea Bay and the Burry Estuary. These strata dip north-eastwards in response to the regional dip of this part of the southern rim of the South Wales Coalfield basin. The succession of solid geological formations represented in Gower is shown in Table 1.

A small outcrop of Triassic rocks occurs at Port-Eynon and numerous fault zones contain red material which may also possibly be Triassic, but no further Mesozoic rocks (245-65 million years before present (MYBP)) occur on land. A long-running controversy exists about a former cover of Jurassic and Cretaceous rocks upon which the present drainage system of South Wales (and southern England) originated, eventually to be superimposed upon the underlying Palaeozoic rocks (570-245 MYBP). Substance is lent to this theory by the presence of Liassic rocks (early Jurassic, 208-178 MYBP) in the Vale of Glamorgan and the presence of Liassic rocks on the sea floor a short distance off the south Gower coast. The former presence, or absence, of a Mesozoic cover is not directly relevant to the present discussion, but a small remnant of Triassic rock on the floor of the valley at Port-Eynon is significant because it proves that some of the relief of Gower was already in existence in Triassic times. This suggests that much of the lower-lying land of South Wales, including

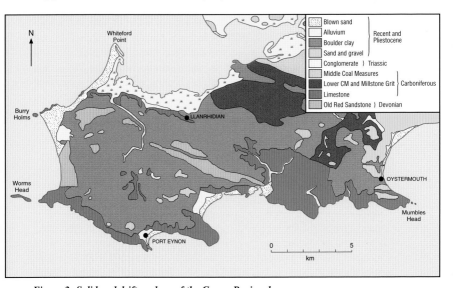

Figure 2: Solid and drift geology of the Gower Peninsula.

7

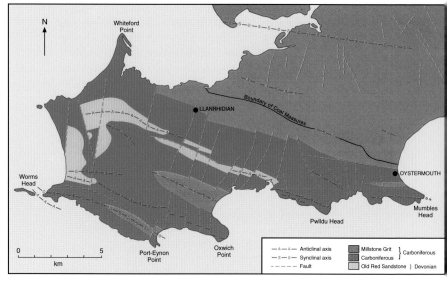

Figure 3: Geological structure of the Palaezoic rocks of the Gower Peninsula.

Table 1: Geological divisions and their lithology

System	Million years BP	Unit	Lithology
Triassic	208-245	Penarth Group	Conglomerate
Carboniferous	290-362	Coal Measures Millstone Grit Carboniferous Limestone	Sandstones, shales and coals Sandstones and shales Limestones and shales
Devonian	362.5-408	Old Red Sandstone	Conglomerates and sandstones

Swansea Bay and Gower, may have been buried by unconsolidated Mesozoic deposits. If Triassic and Jurassic formations ever covered Gower, then all were removed by the Tertiary when the landscape may have been trimmed by the sea to give the well-known examples of **marine abrasion platforms** at 60m, 130m and 180m above present sea-level (Figure 4).

The geological history of Gower is completed by events in the Pleistocene (Table 2) and Holocene (Recent) times. Traditionally the Pleistocene has been sub-divided into 'glacials' and 'interglacials', but in recent years interpretations have depended more upon the nature of the lithostratigraphical units present which reflect the nature of the environment prevailing at the time they were formed. Evidence from Gower has figured significantly in unravelling the succession of events during the later phases of the Pleistocene. Gower was invaded at least twice by ice-sheets which left behind sediments of different character. These deposits originate from three main source areas: from the Irish Sea basin, from Central Wales and from the South Wales Coalfield and Breconshire. The earliest known glaciation which took place is represented by isolated deposits of **till**, sands and gravels scattered throughout South Wales which contain microgranite from the Scottish island of Ailsa Craig. This material had been moved by ice from west to east with deposits occurring as far east as Cowbridge (SS 999740) in the Vale of Glamorgan. In recent literature these deposits have been attributed to the **Anglian** in age (478-423 000 years BP). These older superficial deposits of Gower are mixed with outwash material from the South Wales Coalfield and lie outside the limits of the later **Devensian** glaciation. The second major period of glaciation, the Devensian, saw the accumulation of ice on the uplands of South Wales and the extension of glaciers down the major valleys to impinge on the northern part of the Gower Peninsula, and extend as a **piedmont glacier** onto the floor of Swansea and Carmarthen Bays.

Controversy exists over the extent of ice cover in Gower during the Devensian; some opinions about the location of the ice margin are indicated in Figure 5; further amplification for Gower is given by Bowen (1981), Bridges (1985) and Campbell and Bowen (1989). It was during this final glacial episode, particularly as the ice was melting and its margin receding, that several of the anomalous drainage features of Gower were established as a result of meltwater streams in, below, or alongside the decaying ice (Figure 4). Ice-free areas were affected strongly by solifluction and the glacial deposits were redistributed.

The raised beaches of Gower have intrigued geologists and observant visitors to Gower for many years (George, 1932).

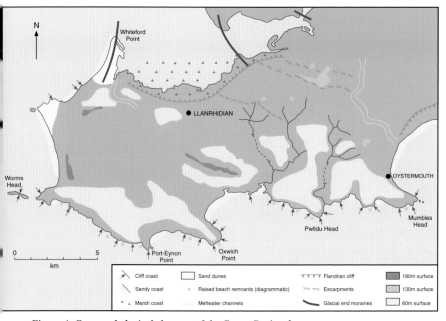

Figure 4: Geomorphological elements of the Gower Peninsula.

Table 2: Simplified chronology of Pleistocene events in Gower

Era		Oxygen Isotope Stage	Approx. age '000 years BP	Location			
				Langland Bay	Deep Slade	Minchin Hole Cave	Port-Eynon
D E V E N S I A N	Late	2		loess	loess	inner and outer talus mounds	loess
			24	Glaciation	Periglacial climate		Periglacial climate formation of terrace
	Middle	3		Cold but short warm intervals	Solifluction of soils and earlier till		Solifluction of earlier till
	Early	4		Angular limestone Head	Angular limestone Head	cave breccias	Angular limestone Head
			122				
IPSWICHIAN		5e		Raised beaches	Raised beaches	Raised beaches	Raised beaches
			128				
WOLSTONIAN		8		Glaciation (Paviland) with similar extent to Devensian			
			303				
ANGLIAN		12		Complete glaciation – maximum extent of ice sheets in Britain			
			478				

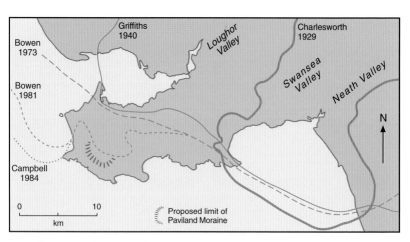

Figure 5: Ice limits according to several authors. *After: Campbell and Bowen, 1989.*

Composed of sand, pebbles and shells cemented with calcium carbonate, they are emplaced on elevated wave-cut platforms on the limestone cliffs. In the past they have generally been attributed to the last interglacial or **Ipswichian** stage (around 125 000 BP) but recent research has shown that the raised beaches have a range of ages, some pre-dating the Ipswichian stage.

Geological events in Holocene times have been dominated by the post-glacial rise in sea-level and the cutting of low cliffs in the redistributed glacial deposits of Gower and Swansea Bay during the **Flandrian transgression** (between 10 000 and 5000 BP). The higher sea-level also enabled the deposition of sediment to take place in the calm waters behind the morainic dumps at the mouth of the Burry Estuary where they now form the basis of Llanrhidian Marsh.

The rising waters of the Flandrian transgression swept before them a considerable quantity of sand, derived from outwash materials from what is now the floor of the Bristol Channel. This mass of sand came to rest in the coves along the limestone cliff coast, and particularly in Swansea, Oxwich, Port-Eynon and Rhossili Bays. Subsequently, a period of extra storminess between the fourteenth and eighteenth centuries (combined perhaps with grazing pressure on the dunes) resulted in the re-mobilisation and migration of sand dunes inland from the coast causing farm lands (and villages) to be abandoned.

Methods of dating

Methods of dating Pleistocene deposits can be described as relative or absolute, with all of them having some limitations. The relative age of a sequence of beds of different lithologies can be determined by assuming that the lowest bed is the oldest and that all beds above must be younger (the geologist's 'Law of Superposition'). In this method the position of a bed indicates its relative age. However, some care must be exercised as solifluction can lead to an inverted sequence of deposits at the foot of slopes from which the youngest materials were the first to be washed off and hence lie beneath redistributed older materials.

From the lithology of the deposit, much can be deduced about the events surrounding deposition. Lithostratigraphy is the contemporary way of evaluating deposits of rock material according to their intrinsic characteristics. For example, a **diamicton** is a specific type of deposit with a particular mix of rock sizes comprising material which, it is thought, has a common origin. The character of the beds, the particle-size, range of materials included, and geomorphology enable an interpretation of their origin to be made.

Biostratigraphy is the means whereby rock deposits are sub-divided according to their fossil content. Because fossils do not persist in glacial tills, it is not always possible to use this dating method on Gower, however it can be useful in marine deposits where *Mollusca* such as snails, bivalves and limpets become incorporated and preserved. Non-marine snails have been used for reconstructing environmental conditions for surface layers, as have pollen grains extracted from soils and peats, and these enable a relationship to be seen with climate change. Certain layers of sediment occurring in Gower caves contain both large and small mammalian fossils which have provided an indication of the date and environmental conditions at the time of their interment.

Absolute dating may be accomplished in several ways. The radio-carbon method is based on the content of ^{14}C present in organic materials incorporated within a mineral deposit. The rate of accumulation of ^{14}C in plants and animals is known, and as ^{14}C decays at a geometric rate with age, a measure of the amount remaining can give satisfactory dates for organic remains over the last 30 000 BP. For older deposits the method is unreliable and even within the effective limits of the method it is difficult to ensure that samples have not been contaminated by roots and carbon of a more recent origin. An alternative absolute method of dating uses amino acids within fossil organic materials; those which have decayed are compared with those which have not and a ratio is calculated. This method enables the time-scale to be extended beyond that achieved by ^{14}C dating.

A completely independent time-scale has been established by analysis of the $^{18}O/^{16}O$ ratio in organisms preserved in oceanic sediments. As these organisms reflect changes in the composition of the oceans, and the isotopic content in turn is controlled by the volume of ice, the ratio gives a basic framework for dating events during the Pleistocene.

THE LIMESTONE CLIFFS OF GOWER

Photo 1: Great Tor, Oxwich Bay. *A typical example of a Gower limestone cliff.*
Photo: EM Bridges.

The broad outline of the south Gower coast is reflected in the folds of the Carboniferous Limestone (Bridges, 1970; 1990). From The Mumbles (SS 621879) westwards, a succession of **anticlines** and **synclines** intersect the coast at an acute angle (see Figure 3, page 8). Mumbles Head, Pwlldu Head, Oxwich Point, Port-Eynon Point and Worms Head are all anticlinal features and the larger bays between them are formed by the intervening synclines. This broad pattern is complicated by many faults, including several major ones, which trend in a north to south direction (Figure 3). Earth movements have imparted a tightly-folded nature to the rocks so the dip encountered at different places along the south Gower coast ranges from almost horizontal to angles up to (Photo 1) and even beyond vertical. Examples may be seen of rocks which dip inland and towards the sea (as at Langland Bay).

The south Gower coast from Mumbles Head to Worms Head has cliffs which, to all intents, are fossil as they are no longer under attack by the sea. Although textbooks may refer to the influence of structure upon the stability of cliff forms, there is currently little active erosion of the solid rocks of the Gower coast. The most active geomorphological processes on these cliffs are sub-aerial: only a narrow zone of solifluction debris at the foot of the cliffs is currently being attacked by marine erosion, and the amount of material being moved is small. At low tide a shore platform can be seen at the foot of the cliffs, truncating the limestone strata. Most of the wave energy is dissipated upon the shore platform which was cut at some unknown time in the past and is not the product of contemporary processes. The presence of unconsolidated solifluction and glacial deposits, as well as raised beaches on the limestone cliffs (Photo 2), is evidence of very little erosion being accomplished during the 10 000 years of Recent geological time (Bowen, 1973).

The origin of various slope deposits on the Gower cliffs can be traced to processes which were active during the last glacial or succeeding **periglacial** periods. Frost-shattered scree material mantles many slopes below protruding buttresses of limestone which form the edge of the plateau at about 60m (Figure 6). Much of this fossil scree is covered by vegetation and a thin **rendzina** soil has developed on slopes of 30-35°, but areas can still be seen where active scree occurs at the surface. Towards the foot of the fossil cliff the scree has been cemented by calcium carbonate and forms overhanging masses (Figure 9). Glacial drift from two periods of glaciation may also be seen on the cliff slopes.

Photo 2: Raised beach overlooked by fossil cliffs, Mewslade Bay.
Photo: Christopher Green.

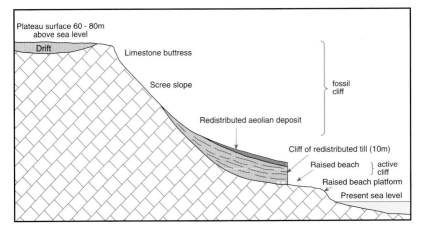

Figure 6: Elements of a south Gower cliff profile.

East of Langland Bay, till and glacio-fluvial material of Devensian age lie on the cliff slopes. Further westwards, pre-Devensian materials occur at the foot of the cliffs where they have been re-deposited by solifluction. Lastly, there is the presence of an aeolian deposit (**loess**) derived from former outwash plains, lying to the south of Gower and now covered by the sea. This loess has been partly re-deposited by periglacial processes as is indicated by the presence of stones. The loess occupies the upper metre of many coastal sections west of the assumed Devensian ice margin. All these features may be observed along footpaths on the south coast of Gower: specific features and their locations are described in the following sections on Mumbles and Langland Bay, Pwlldu Head to Threecliff Bay and Oxwich Point to Rhossili.

MUMBLES AND LANGLAND BAY

Photo 3: Bracelet Bay and Mumbles Head. *Photo: EM Bridges.*

Mumbles Head (Photo 3) is the easternmost extremity of the Gower Peninsula. An anticlinal flexure of the Carboniferous Limestone can be seen on the right-hand side of the B4433 from Oystermouth to the headland. The rocks revealed in this outcrop dip steeply towards the north-east and form the northern limb of the anticline. Before reaching the headland, the road passes through a cutting which also shows the north-easterly dip. At the headland, the road turns south-westwards and crosses the axis of the anticline at the rear of Bracelet (SS 630870) and Limeslade (SS 626870) Bays. South-westerly-dipping strata can be seen on Tutt Head (SS 628871) between Bracelet and Limeslade Bays (Figure 7).

Mumbles Head is formed of two small islands (Photo 3), the geological structure of which can readily be appreciated from the mainland. Hollowed out of the rocks on the Outer Head is Bob's Cave (SS 635872), this is at the centre of the anticline which pitches south-eastwards. Evidence of the north to south pattern of faulting can be appreciated at Mumbles Head where faults separate the two islands from the mainland, but also between The Knab (SS 626876) and Limeslade Bay where a deep gash in the rocks, known locally as 'The Cut', has been excavated for iron ore in the past. Although almost completely refilled, its position can be seen clearly in the field and on the 1:25 000 map. Limeslade Bay has been eroded at the southern end of this fault which contained the iron-rich deposits sought by miners. Despite the complexity of the underlying geological structure of Mumbles Head, seen from West Cross (SS 615895) it has an almost level summit surface at about 60m above sea-level.

At Langland Bay, the south-western limb of the Mumbles Anticline has been breached by the sea and the Carboniferous Limestone dips seawards on both sides of the Bay. The limestone cliffs east of Langland are partly covered by unconsolidated glacio-fluvial deposits which form a low cliff of about 14m at the rear of the shore platform. At the base of this cliff section (SS 613871) the drift is grey in colour and more compact. This is covered by a brown stony drift, composed of glacio-fluvial material and till, crudely stratified with indications of having been deposited close to the margin of the Devensian ice sheet. The section is capped by a thin layer (about 1m) of almost stoneless silty drift, interpreted as a redistributed and decalcified loess. The origin of this silty material is from the outwash deposits lying on the floor of the Bristol Channel in the immediate post-glacial period when sea-levels were low. Wind, blowing over the outwash, lifted the silt and deposited some of it on the adjacent higher land.

At certain places along this section of the coast an orange-brown sandy material containing limestone fragments can be seen to lie between the drift and the raised beach platform upon which it rests. This deposit has been interpreted as blown sand from the foreshore to which has been added frost-shattered debris and soliflucted soil material. The sand was exposed as the sea-level fell, and the frost shattered debris accumulated as a result of the onset of the colder conditions associated with the advance of the Devensian ice sheet.

Access
There is a car park (SS 628872) on the western side of Bracelet Bay from which both Mumbles Head, to the east, and Limeslade Bay, to the west, are accessible. At low tide it is possible to walk across to the Outer Head. Almost beneath the lighthouse on the Outer Head you will find Bob's Cave (SS 635872). **Do check the times of the tides before you go out.**

Langland Bay car park (SS 605874) offers easy access to Langland Bay itself. Both Bracelet Bay and Langland Bay car parks are capable of accommodating coaches.

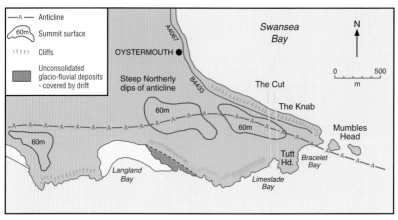

Figure 7: Geomorphological elements of the Mumbles and Langland Bay, showing the axis of the Mumbles Anticline.

PWLLDU HEAD TO THREECLIFF BAY

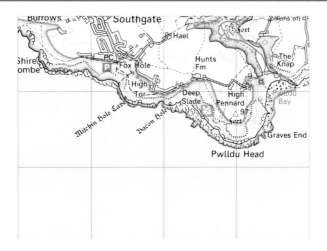

This stretch of the Gower coast, with its raised beaches and caves, is probably the most interesting as well as being easily accessible. Pwlldu Head (SS 570863) is an anticlinal headland and, like Mumbles, is capped by a plateau-like surface at 60-65m above sea-level. Immediately to the west of Pwlldu Head is Hunt's Bay (SS 564866) and a small valley leading inland known as Deep Slade. The two large caves of Bacon Hole (SS 561868) and Minchin Hole Cave (SS 555869 – labelled Mitchin Hole Cave on OS Landranger sheet 159) are situated in the cliffs between Hunt's Bay and Heatherslade Bay (SS 550871) just south of Southgate. Remnants of raised beach are common all along the stretch from Pwlldu Head to Threecliff Bay (see Photo 2 (page 14) and the Ordnance Survey extract above).

A raised beach is clear evidence that the relationship between land and sea has altered: either sea-level has changed or there has been movement of the land relative to the sea. Raised beach remnants may be seen at many places along the Gower coast, but some of the best examples occur at Hunt's Bay and Heatherslade Bay. In Heatherslade Bay just before crossing onto the bare rocks at the foot of the slope (SS 554870) there is a low cliff in solifluction debris. At the foot of this low cliff, and emerging from beneath it, is an elevated, dissected shore platform. At several places on this shore platform, about 8m above sea-level, is a cemented pebbly deposit, firmly grouted into the Carboniferous Limestone rocks (Photo 4). The pebbles of this deposit

Photo 4: Heatherslade Bay raised beach. *Photo: EM Bridges.*

are well-rounded, consisting mainly of limestone, but including other rocks as well as fossils of the gastropod *Patella vulgata*, a limpet which has given its name to this raised beach – the Patella beach. The pebbles and the included fossils are all cemented together with calcium carbonate.

The floor of Heatherslade Bay is characterised by a shore platform which is partly covered with sand. A casual inspection of this lower platform might suggest it relates to the present sea-level, however, on the eastern side of the bay another remnant of cemented pebbles with sand and fossils rests on this surface and has been called the Heatherslade raised beach. The remnant is eroded and little remains, but it is, without doubt, similar to the material of the Patella raised beach. It too, consists mainly of rounded limestone fragments but contains a greater quantity of far-travelled material from the South Wales Coalfield rocks than the higher Patella beach. A lower sea-level in the Devensian and a higher one in the Flandrian have both occurred since this beach remnant was deposited and now the sea has returned to approximately the same level as when it was laid down. As it lies in the zone of the breaking waves, this lower beach remnant is being gradually eroded. Raised beach material has also been preserved in Bacon Hole and Minchin Hole caves (see page 23) which has enabled more detail to be established about the events of late Pleistocene and Recent times (Campbell and Bowen, 1989).

A consensus has long held that the Patella beach is all of one age, dating from the Ipswichian interglacial. The amino acid ratio of fossils in the raised beaches has confirmed an Ipswichian date for most of these raised beaches, but has also revealed a range of dates, some of which pre-date the Ipswichian Stage. This interglacial stage may have been warmer (by an average of 1-2°C) than the present-day climate because red soils, like the *terra rossa* found in the Mediterranean countries, were developed over the limestone. However, there is the possibility that these red soils may be the remnants of a former Triassic cover, see page **. As the Devensian glaciation began, these soils were the first to be affected by solifluction and moved over the edge of the plateau and down the fossil cliffs onto the Patella raised beach. Frost-shattering of the limestone contributed the angular limestone fragments which can be seen interlayered with the red soils on the western side of Hunt's Bay (SS 562868) (Photo 5). This re-deposited soil material passes upwards into crudely stratified solifluction material with increasing numbers of far-travelled pebbles in the upper layers. At the centre of the Bay, the low cliff is composed of frost-shattered rock fragments in a variable matrix which obviously has a South Wales Coalfield provenance, rather than a local Gower origin. Scree cemented with calcium carbonate may be seen upslope of this section (Figure 8).

Examination of the stones comprising these deposits indicates that they are not lying in a random manner (Figure 9). If the direction of the long axes of a number of the stones is plotted, a strong orientation downslope is apparent thus confirming the role of solifluction in their accumulation. The upper 1 to 1.5m of the low cliff at the back of the beach at Hunt's Bay comprises silt which is regarded as having an

Photo 5: Layered angular limestone fragments and soil material at Hunt's Bay.
Photo: EM Bridges.

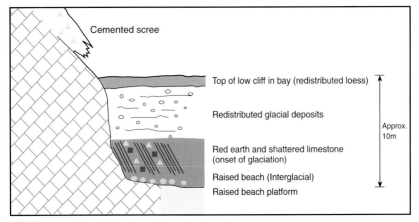

Figure 8: Section of deposits at Hunts Bay (west).

aeolian origin. However, as the silt contains the occasional pebble, flint cores and blades, it too is thought to have accumulated and subsequently moved downslope as a solifluction deposit.

Minchin Hole and Bacon Hole caves

There are several large caves along the coast of Gower, developed where faults occur in the Carboniferous Limestone cliffs. At times of high sea-level, the sea has exploited the weaknesses of a fault zone to excavate a cave in which beach materials accumulated. When the sea-level dropped, during the cold conditions of glaciation (Devensian), enlargement of caves took place by frost action, with frost-shattered debris falling from the roof to accumulate on the cave floor. During this period the caves also acted as places of shelter for animals and people. On the face of the cliffs frost-shattered debris partially, or even completely, buried the

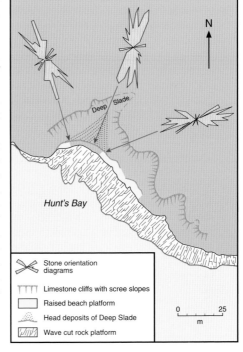

Figure 9: Stone orientation diagrams at Hunt's Bay.
After: Harris, 1973.

21

cave entrances, sealing inside the deposits which often included fossils. When sea-level rose again after the Devensian glaciation, the caves began to be re-exposed as the frost-shattered debris was eroded and washed away (Figure 10).

Extinct animal bones were discovered in a cave near Nicholaston (SS 520880) as early as 1792. During the nineteenth century it became fashionable to excavate the caves for the remains of straight-tusked elephant, narrow-nosed rhinoceros, mammoth, bison, reindeer, cave bear, wolf and hyena. Unfortunately, both amateur and professional collectors of the last century dug in an unscientific manner with the result that much valuable information about former climate change, with which the deposits and fossils were associated, has been lost (see Paviland Cave – pages 28-29).

Although group visits are not recommended to Bacon Hole (SS 561868) and Minchin Hole Cave (SS 555869) both caves are well worth a mention. They have yielded much information about environmental conditions during the last major stage of glaciation, the Devensian (Stringer, 1977). Within Minchin Hole Cave the following sequence of deposits has been described upwards from the floor of the cave:

(i) An inner beach, composed of bedded grey sand with fine shingle layers, containing a pre-Ipswichian faunal assemblage dated 210 000 BP. This beach lies upon a wave-smoothed rock floor and it is covered by an incipient stalagmitic crust. The pre-Devensian sea-level was at least 3m higher than at present.

(ii) A lower red **cave earth** containing some mammalian remains including the narrow-nosed rhinoceros and northern vole. There is evidence of a stalagmitic crust deposited over this material.

(iii) An outer beach – the Patella beach. This was formed at a time of higher sea-level and was cut into the lower cave earth. It contains a mixture of boulder, shingle, sand and shell fragments dated at 125 000 BP. It lies between 6.2m and 12.4m OD and is embanked against the inner beach and lower cave earth.

(iv) A pink sandy clay overlies the Patella beach on the western wall of the cave. It contains gastropods and formerly was thought to be another, higher raised beach (the Neritoides beach) but is now interpreted as a transition from the Patella beach to the overlying cave earth.

(v) Brown cave earth with limestone fragments containing abundant mammalian and bird remains. An interglacial fauna including narrow-nosed rhinoceros, elephant, red and fallow deer, pig, lion, spotted hyena, red fox, bank vole, field vole, and in the upper part, northern vole. This evidence suggests a warm interglacial climate which subsequently turned colder.

(vi) (a) inner and (b) outer **talus** mounds. The outer talus mound has largely been eroded and can only be seen as fragments of limestone and aeolian material adhering to the cave walls near the entrance. The inner talus mound consists of angular limestone blocks in a matrix of a red cave earth and is covered by a thick stalagmitic crust (Bowen and Henry, 1984; Campbell and Bowen, 1989).

Beaches extend over a significant height range and this has not made correlation of scattered remnants easy. However, from the sequence of deposits in the caves it can be appreciated that they were formed at different levels and at different times. The Neritoides beach referred to above in (iv) is a case in point. However, recent dating by the amino acid technique indicates that both Patella and Neritoides beaches were Ipswichian in age.

The outer talus mound formerly blocked the cave entrance and preserved the deposits inside. Whilst the full implications of this sequence are not completely understood (and can be interpreted in different ways) it appears that the cave earths represent cold periods with low sea-levels and the raised beaches and high sea-levels represent warmer intervals. Minchin Hole Cave contains the longest continuous sedimentary record of the late Pleistocene in Wales and with its evidence of two high sea-levels is a site of international geological importance. Investigations of Bacon Hole indicate a similar succession of deposits and confirm the general sequence of events and, in addition, it includes a more complete faunal record.

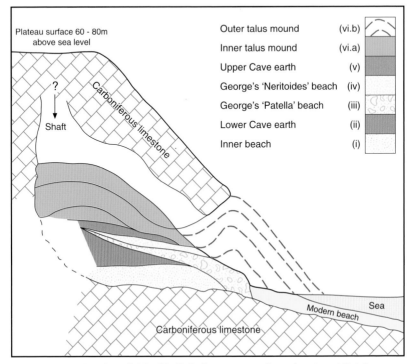

Figure 10: Section through Minchin Hole Cave – see text for explanation of (i)-(vi). *After: Campbell and Bowen, 1989.*

The faunal sequence (Campbell and Bowen, 1989) can be related to the independent oxygen isotope chronology established for deep sea sediments.

Threecliff Bay

Between Heatherslade Bay and Threecliff Bay, the coast is formed by cliffs in which the steeply dipping limestone strata can be seen to be overfolded. At Threecliff Bay, the steep dip and faulting have combined to give the three pyramidal peaks which give the bay its name. There is a cave which penetrates through the inclined limestone strata to give a natural arch (Photo 6). The western extremity of the bay is marked by Great Tor (SS 530876) where the bedding planes of the limestone are vertical (Figure 11 and Photo 1).

Pennard Pill (a stream with karstic features) flows into the sea at Threecliff Bay after following a deeply incised course across the limestone outcrop. Unpublished seismic evidence from the valley south of Parkmill Village suggests it was occupied by glacier ice and over-deepened by glacial scouring. Subsequently, the floor of the valley has been partly infilled by Late Glacial or Holocene deposits (10 000 BP) similar to those described for the Ilston Valley (SS 558905) (Saunders *et al.*, 1989). The seaward end of Pennard Pill Valley is partly barred by a low beach shingle ridge, composed of

Photo 6: At Threecliff Bay the steeply dipping limestone rocks include a natural arch. Photo: EM Bridges.

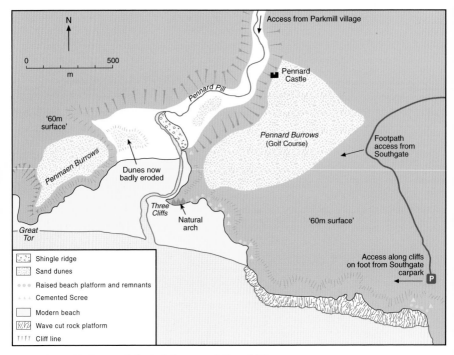

Figure 11: Geomorphological elements of Threecliff Bay.

partly rounded, platey limestone fragments, extending out from the eastern side of the valley. The Pennard Pill meanders over the alluvial infill and escapes seawards around the western end of this low beach ridge. Where the beach ridge meets the valley side an exposure of scree, composed of angular frost-shattered clasts cemented by calcium carbonate, may be inspected. This can be compared with the raised beach materials on the adjacent cliff face.

Until the mid-1960s, a sand dune system (Penmaen Burrows) extended from the western side of the bay causing the stream to be diverted across the front of the beach ridge. Although the sand dunes have been seriously reduced in recent years, the stream still maintains its course on the eastern side of the valley and enters the open sea immediately west of the limestone outcrop forming the three cliffs.

The high tidal range of the Bristol Channel leaves a large area of sand between low and high water marks exposed, and the prevailing wind has blown sand into the Pennard Pill Valley where dunes occur. This wind has also blown sand up the eastern side of the valley where the castle and former village of Pennard were eventually overwhelmed – historical records reveal that extra storminess began in the fourteenth century; the church near Pennard Castle was abandoned in the sixteenth century and sand incursion continued until the end of the eighteenth century (Photo 7). In 1535, the vicar of Pennard complained to the King's Commissioners that his church,

Photo 7: Pennard Castle surrounded by sand which covers the eastern valley side and extends onto the plateau. *Photo: EM Bridges.*

house and glebe land on the valley floor were being affected by 'the drift sands of the sea' causing tenancies to be vacated and reducing his income (Toft, 1988).

Access

Exposures of the raised beaches at Heatherslade Bay are best approached by following the footpath down from the car park (SS 554873) at Southgate.

Bacon Hole and Minchin Hole caves can only be approached by difficult, dangerous cliff paths and are not recommended for class visits. The deposits within the caves can be viewed, **but must not be disturbed by unauthorised digging.**

Access to Pennard Pill Valley is via a footpath from Parkmill, where parking (charge) is associated with the Gower Heritage Centre (Tel: 01792 371206). It is free for visitors to the centre. Alternatively, park at the Southgate car park, walk along the cliffs and clamber over the headland with the Three Cliffs.

OXWICH POINT TO RHOSSILI

South of the hamlets of Oxwich Green and Slade, the coastal path from Oxwich Point (SS 514850) to Port-Eynon Point (SS 472845) follows the edge of an interesting **solifluction terrace.** This terrace lies in front of the Carboniferous Limestone cliffs, it is about 100m wide and its surface is at an elevation of 15m above sea-level. In the terrace, which rests upon the shore platform and in places upon small areas of Ipswichian raised beach (3.5-4m above sea-level), layers of coarse **head** in a red matrix can be seen. This in turn is overlaid by a finer deposit of head derived by solifluction from the 'Paviland' glacial drift lying on the plateau surface to the north. The uppermost layer of the terrace deposits is a silty drift of loessial material which smoothly covers any irregularities in the coarser head beneath.

The material forming this terrace was derived from pre-Ipswichian glacial debris left upon the plateau surface north of Slade and Port-Eynon. It includes pebbles of Ailsa Craig microgranite and fragments of local South Wales sandstone (Figure 12a). Originally thought of as an *in situ* glacial deposit, this terrace consists of re-worked older material which indicates that this part of south-west Gower was not subject to invasion by Devensian ice. The three small dry valleys leading southwards from the limestone plateau acted as channels along which drift material was transported by solifluction in a periglacial environment (Figure 12b). The re-deposited materials have a fan-like form, extending from the mouths of the small valleys which provides morphological evidence of where the materials originated.

The South Gower National Nature Reserve

From Port-Eynon Point to the village of Rhossili the cliffs of Gower are a National Nature Reserve administered by the Countryside Council for Wales and owned jointly by the National Trust and the Glamorgan Wildlife Trust (see Contents page). Two major caves are situated on this part of the coast: Longhole Cave (SS 452851) and Paviland Cave (SS 438859).

Longhole Cave contains sediments which relate to changing climatic conditions throughout the Ipswichian and Devensian stages of the Pleistocene. It also contains archaeological evidence of human occupation. An analysis of pollen preserved in the sediments suggests milder conditions and temperate woodland being followed by a prolonged period of arctic tundra conditions. Boreal conditions appeared about 65 000 BP and are associated with the appearance of Palaeolithic artefacts preserved in the cave sediments.

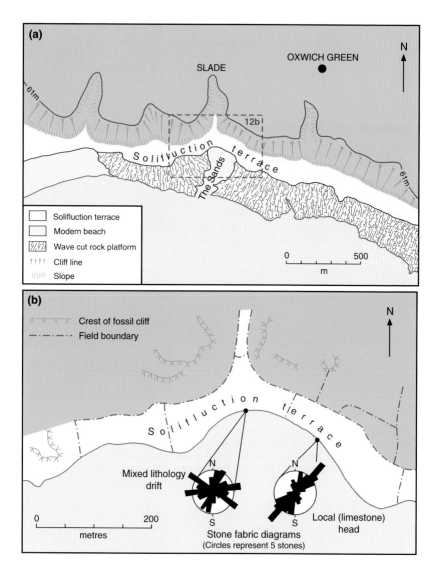

Figure 12: (a) Solifluction terrace and (b) stone orientation diagrams at Slade.

The most famous of Gower's caves is Paviland Cave which contained one of the richest Palaeolithic archaeological finds in Britain. In 1823, Professor Dean Buckland of Oxford University excavated Paviland Cave and discovered a headless human skeleton covered in red ochre, apparently buried with ivory trinkets. In addition, over 800 stone implements and the bones of several animals were also excavated. The skeleton was named the 'Red Lady of Paviland'. Later studies established this skeleton to be male, at first with a date of c. 18 500 BP – coinciding with the maximum extent of ice cover in the Devensian, but more recently revised to 24 000 BP which places it before this maximum. The bones of the 'Red Lady'

Photo 8: Worms Head (part of the South Gower NNR). The wave cut platform serves as a natural causeway. Photo: Christopher Green.

now reside in the University Museum in Oxford and a reconstruction can be seen in Cardiff Museum.

At the western extremity of the Gower Peninsula is Worms Head (SS 384877) and Rhossili (Figure 13). It is immediately obvious that the surface of the headland has a plateau-like appearance at 60m above sea-level, and that this surface is cut across the Carboniferous Limestone strata – which are here in the form of a fractured anticline (see Figure 3).

Forty years ago a buried red soil was found at Worms Head (Ball, 1960) which, from its appearance, mineralogy and micro-structure resembled soils currently found in Mediterranean countries. Originally thought to be *in situ*, it was concluded that this soil had formed in somewhat warmer conditions than are experienced at present. Subsequent studies have preferred to regard this 'soil' as being colluvial, having been subject to solifluction as the climate deteriorated at the beginning of the Devensian glaciation. It was later covered by a mixed lithology drift or outwash material at the time of the maximum Devensian ice extent. Remnants of raised beaches can be seen on both inner and outer parts of the island dated, as elsewhere on the Gower coast, to the Ipswichian stage (125 000 BP) (Campbell and Bowen, 1989). The surface of the Inner Head (SS 394875) has a remarkably level appearance at about 30m above sea-level. The Inner and Outer Heads of Worms Head are joined by a natural bridge known locally as 'Devil's Bridge' (Photo 9).

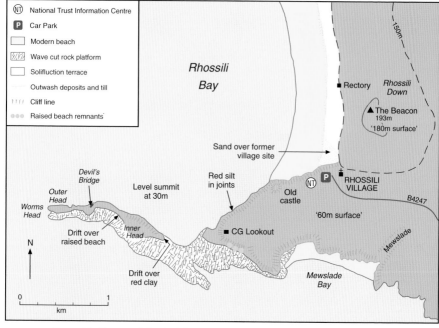

Figure 13: Geomorphological elements of Rhossili and Worms Head.

Access

Similar features occur on this stretch of coast to those described previously in this guide but they are less accessible; school parties and large groups should not normally be brought to this part of the Gower coast.

Car parks are situated at Oxwich (SS 503865), Horton (SS 474855), Port-Eynon (SS 467852) and Rhossili (SS 415879).

The solifluction terrace south of Oxwich Green and Slade can be reached on foot from Oxwich car park following footpaths (5km return walk) from the two hamlets. Alternatively, the coastal footpath around Oxwich Point (8km return walk) or from Horton car park (4km return walk) can be used.

The coast between Port Eynon and Rhossili can be reached by the footpath from car parks at either end. Access to Paviland Cave is also possible by a footpath from the B4247 at Pilton Green.

Rhossili and the island of Worms Head is part of the South Gower National Nature Reserve and a National Trust shop and advisory centre are situated in the former coastguard cottages near the car park (SS 415880) at Rhossili. You should not visit the island between mid-March and July to avoid disturbing birds during the nesting season, nor should you pick wild flowers or enter any fenced areas (where schemes to counter erosion are in operation). Visitors are welcome to walk to the end of the headland where there is a small information centre (open during the holiday season) in the old coastguard lookout.

Photo 9: The Devil's Bridge, Worms Head. Photo: EM Bridges.

Safety note

If you propose to visit the island of Worms Head follow the falling tide out and bear in mind that there are only about two-and-a-half hours on either side of low tide when it is possible to walk across the causeway to the island. Tidal currents between the headland and island are very strong and on no account should swimming be contemplated.

THE SANDY SHORES OF GOWER

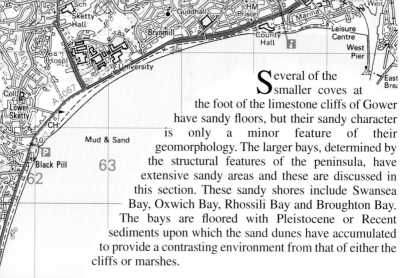

Several of the smaller coves at the foot of the limestone cliffs of Gower have sandy floors, but their sandy character is only a minor feature of their geomorphology. The larger bays, determined by the structural features of the peninsula, have extensive sandy areas and these are discussed in this section. These sandy shores include Swansea Bay, Oxwich Bay, Rhossili Bay and Broughton Bay. The bays are floored with Pleistocene or Recent sediments upon which the sand dunes have accumulated to provide a contrasting environment from that of either the cliffs or marshes.

Swansea Bay

Swansea Bay lies to the east of the Gower peninsula where a 15km wide inlet of the sea is partly protected by Mumbles Head from the exposed waters of the Bristol Channel. In Swansea Bay, the rim of the South Wales Coalfield basin is breached by down faulting of the Carboniferous Limestone, Millstone Grit and Coal Measures (see Figures 2 and 3). This structure may be associated with the strong north-east to south-west faulting of the Neath and Swansea valleys, the abrupt, faulted western end of the Vale of Glamorgan and the east to west Moel Gilau disturbance of the South Wales Coalfield. It has been hypothesised that the lowland of the bay might have been infilled by unconsolidated Triassic deposits; but these have subsequently been removed by erosion (see Cefn Bryn, pages 45-46).

During the Pleistocene, ice twice invaded the area and unconsolidated deposits were left behind. On the first occasion, at approximately 450 000 years BP, ice moved from the west towards

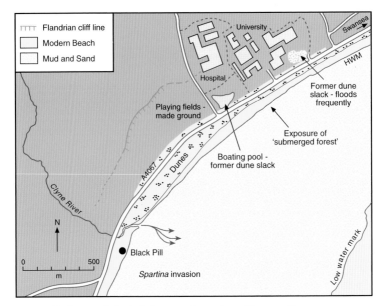

Figure 14: Geomorphological elements of a section of Swansea Bay.

the east, leaving behind a till which has been recognised in south-western Gower and the Vale of Glamorgan. On the second occasion, between 100 000 and 12 000 years BP, ice from the hinterland of the South Wales Coalfield extended down the Neath, Swansea and Loughor valleys to form a piedmont type of glacier in the embayment (Figure 5). Any earlier pre-Ipswichian moraines were re-worked and deep hollows were scooped out of the solid rocks by ice in the Neath and Swansea valleys. Where the ice was constricted off Mumbles Head, hollows 26m deep have been identified in the rock floor of Swansea Bay. These hollows have been infilled with silts and peats to -18m OD. The upper surface of these deposits has been dated at 10 000 years BP, after which the bay was inundated by the Flandrian transgression (Culver, 1976).

Sea-level continued to rise until low cliffs were cut in the glacial deposits on the north-east side of the playing fields at Ashleigh Road (SS 621915) (Figure 14). A slight fall in sea-level since has revealed an extensive area of sand for the wind to act upon to form a dune landscape. No obvious structure in the dunes of Swansea Bay is apparent as the dunes are much degraded and have been grassed over to form a golf course. A former railway track also crossed the dunes before entering the Clyne Valley at Black Pill (SS 620905). Behind the dunes an area of wet, peaty birch woodland developed during the Iron Age (c. 2500 years BP). Gradual inland movement of the dunes has overwhelmed some of this woodland; tree stumps, still in their growth position, can sometimes be seen on the foreshore (Photo 10) between the entrance of the University and Sketty Lane where they formerly grew in a very poorly drained soil. Inland of the dunes, the level of this low-lying land has been raised by refuse tipping to form

Photo 10: Remnants of the submerged forest, Swansea Bay. *Photo: EM Bridges.*

playing fields but within the confines of Singleton Park a former **dune slack** has been converted into a boating pool, and in the meadow in front of Singleton Abbey, flooding frequently occurs.

The greater amount of sand occurs on the eastern and north-eastern sides of Swansea Bay where industrialisation has taken place on former dune landscapes, reflecting the importance of the south-westerly winds on this part of the coast. The western side of the bay has little sand and the east-facing Gower shore is cut either in glacial drift or in Millstone Grit rocks as at West Cross (SS 614895) where a small anticline may be seen on the foreshore. In the lee of Mumbles Head a stony beach occurs on the steeply dipping flank of the Mumbles Head Anticline.

Controversy exists over the supply of sand for the beaches with off-shore dredging and adverse weather being blamed when the beaches are stripped of sand during winter storms. Whatever the cause, there appears to be only a finite amount of sand available; at present very little sand is moving from the floor of Swansea Bay on to the dune system. On the floor of Swansea Bay at Black Pill *Spartina anglica* is attempting to colonise the silty deposits but is being discouraged by the local authority's Environment Department. If it were to be successful, accretion would be rapid and the nature of the foreshore would change considerably.

Oxwich Bay

Oxwich Bay occurs where a synclinal structure including the Carboniferous Limestone and the Limestone Shales reaches the coast. The attractive wooded slopes of Nicholaston and Oxwich Point cover strata dipping steeply towards the centre of the bay. At the head of the bay, the Limestone Shales form the lower-lying land. A small stream, Nicholaston Pill, reaches the sea at the eastern side of Oxwich Bay after its waters have flowed through the formerly landscaped marshes which lie behind the dune system (Figure 15).

The sand dune system, Oxwich Burrows, has a similar origin to the sands of Swansea Bay and the other Gower bays. The enclosed nature of Oxwich Bay (Photo 11) has acted as a trap in which the sand has been caught as it was gradually moved landwards by the rising waters of the Flandrian transgression until it came to rest at the head of the bay. Four different types of dune can be seen at Oxwich: (i) U-shaped dunes, (ii) blow-outs, (iii) foredunes, and (iv) attached dunes.

i. U-shaped dunes

The Oxwich U-shaped dunes have an east-south-east to west-north-west alignment (Figure 16). Although the dominant winds here are north-westerly, they are usually associated with rain and wet conditions so when they blow the sand is less mobile. It is the dry south-easterly winds which are responsible for the formation of U-shaped dunes. The ends of these dunes which point to windward are the first parts to become stabilised, with the central part continuing to migrate inland. Removal of sand between the two arms continues until moist sand near the water-table is reached and a dune slack is initiated. When colonised by vegetation these dune slacks have a more varied plant life than the dunes themselves, owing to the availability of water.

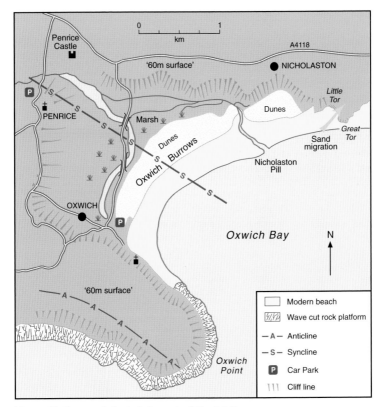

Figure 15: Geomorphological elements of Oxwich Bay.

ii. Blow-outs

Blow-outs are a normal occurrence on dune landscapes and can lead to the formation of trough-like hollows in the dune system (Harris, 1974). These become more common when the dunes come under heavy pressure from humans and in an extreme situation the whole dune system can be destroyed. The western end of Oxwich Burrows dune system is under particular pressure: some has been used as a car park and the Countryside Council for Wales has fenced part of the dunes to protect them from further destruction.

iii. Foredunes

As their name suggest, foredunes occur at the front of the dune system, at the rear of the beach. As accretion is active, these low dunes are frequently colonised by Marram grass which requires a supply of fresh sand to flourish.

iv. Attached dunes

Attached dunes form in the lee of any obstruction to windflow. This may either be vegetation or even be part of a U-shaped dunes described above.

Although the major dune system at Oxwich shows evidence of the south-east winds being dominant in shaping the morphology, it appears that sand migration on the eastern side of the bay near the Great and Little Tors has been in response to the south-west winds. Sand has covered a medieval settlement at Penmaen (SS 526885) where remains of a fortified farmstead and church occur (SS 532882). Movement into the Bishopston valley has already been commented upon.

Photo 11: Oxwich Bay and the coastline of south Gower.
The dunes of Oxwich Burrows can be seen to the centre and left foreground of the photo. Photo: Mark Button.

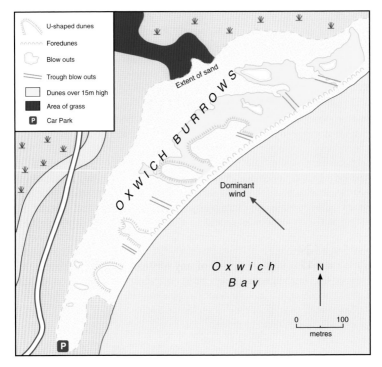

Figure 16: Oxwich Burrows sand dune complex. *After: Harris, 1974.*

Access

Access to the dunes or the marshes at Oxwich is usually possible after obtaining permission from the Countryside Council for Wales (Tel: 01792 771949). The area is one of the National Nature Reserves of the Gower coast and information about the plant and animal life of the reserve may be obtained on request.

Rhossili Bay

The gently shelving, 5km sandy beach at Rhossili is the largest of the Gower beaches. It is situated between two anticlinal flexures in the Carboniferous Limestone which form the promontories of Worms Head and Burry Holms (SS 400925) respectively. The western flank of Rhossili Down is interpreted as a fault scarp, abruptly cutting off the Old Red Sandstone rocks, which in places form tors on the crest of the Down at 180m above sea-level. Between Rhossili Down and the beach a terrace of solifluction debris occurs with a 10-15m high cliff (Figure 13, page 30 and Photo 12). It is argued that west-facing slopes favoured more intense solifluction during periods of periglacial climate. An examination of the material in this low cliff reveals angular local rock material incorporated in a reddish-brown matrix derived from the steep slopes of Old Red Sandstone above.

On the cliffs west of the present village of Rhossili, beyond the banks and ditches of the 'old castle', bright red silty clays occur in joints and overlying the limestone. Microscopic examination of this clay indicates that it is similar to *terra rossa* and unlike any soil forming at present in the area. It may represent a remnant of an interglacial soil of Ipswichian age. This is but one explanation; other suggestions include remnants of a Triassic cover and the influence of calcium weathered from the limestone which causes precipitation of iron and clay in the weathered material immediately above the limestone.

About 1km south of Hillend (SS 419909) at the northern end of Rhossili Down, outwash deposits and till replace the solifluction debris in the low cliff (SS 415898). Below the modern storm beach, a brown clayey till has been observed similar to that found in Broughton Bay. It would appear that ice extended into Rhossili Bay (and, by inference, well into Carmarthen Bay) which is further south than hitherto thought. Till or outwash which has a mixed provenance has already been noted as occurring on Worms Head (page 29). Previously this material had been interpreted as a deposit of the earlier pre-Ipswichian glaciation but, as it can be seen to overlie the Ipswichian raised beach, an alternative explanation is necessary. It may represent late Devensian outwash or it may prove to be evidence for a southward extension of ice into Carmarthen and Rhossili Bays (Campbell and Shakesby, 1994). The original village of Rhossili was situated on the solifluction terrace, where remains of a church and farm buildings have been found beneath the sand dunes. A combination of erosion of the solifluction terrace and besanding eventually led to the site being abandoned for the more exposed site on the plateau.

North of Hillend a beach ridge encloses the low-lying fen of Llangennith Moors. This beach ridge extends to the anticline of limestone which forms the islet of Burry Holms. The solid rocks in this area are covered by sand dunes, which attain a height of 60m. The sand originates from sandbanks lying at the mouth of the River Loughor and from Rhossili beach itself. Bronze Age artefacts found beneath the dunes suggest that sand accumulation took

Photo 12: Rhossili Bay, Rhossili Down. *The solifluction terrace partly covered by sand dunes lies at the rear of the bay. Broughton Burrows and Burry Holms can be seen in the distance. Photo: Mark Button.*

place after that period. Further movement of sand from offshore banks may have taken place during periods of extra storminess from the fourteenth to the eighteenth centuries, as experienced at Pennard and elsewhere in South Wales.

Access

There are car parks at the southern end of Rhossili Bay in Rhossili (SS416879) and at the northern end at Hillend (SS 413909), which offer easy access up to The Beacon on Rhossili Down, onto the solifluction terrace, the dunes and the beach.

Broughton Bay and Whiteford Point

The north-western facet of the Gower coast includes Broughton Bay, backed by glacial drift covered by dunes, and the sand dunes of Whiteford Point.

The foundation of Whiteford Point is a mass of till deposited from ice which occupied the Loughor Valley during the greatest extent of the Devensian glaciation. It is not known how far into Carmarthen Bay this tongue of ice penetrated, nor what its relationship to ice from the Towy Valley might have been. It was formerly thought that the material beneath Whiteford Point was a terminal moraine, but recent exposures in Broughton Bay, west of the Point, have shown Pleistocene sediments of Devensian age (Campbell and Shakesby, 1994).

Erosion of the dunes by the sea at the western end of Broughton Bay has revealed a series of folds in thinly bedded, shelly till (Figure 17). Near to Twlc Point (SS 417930), the limestone headland on the western side of Broughton Bay, the dip of some of these structures increases to 40°. Shells from the till have been dated using ^{14}C and amino acid ratio analysis and are of Late Ipswichian age. The generalised stratigraphical sequence includes:

- blown sand (5m)

- Head with erratics (0.5m)

- soliflucted till (4m)

- shelly till (5m)

- bedded shelly till with folded structures (2.5m)

- head (sand and gravel) (0.5m)

- raised beach

The succession is interpreted as being laid down from late Devensian ice which moved southwards across Carmarthen Bay to deposit the bedded till, including shells of Ipswichian age derived from what is now the sea floor. It is thought that the structures in the bedded till were introduced as a result of the pressures developed when ice passed through the low col between Llanmadoc Down and Burry Holms, over-riding Prissen's Tor (SS 425937) and Hills Tor (SS 428940). However, the detailed interplay of ice from across Carmarthen Bay with ice from the Loughor Valley is unknown. As the climate ameliorated after the Devensian glaciation, vegetation re-

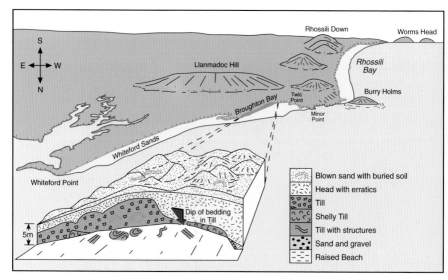

Figure 17: Geomorphological elements of Broughton Bay. *After: Shakesby and Campbell, 1985.*

established itself on the floor of the estuary, sea-level being lower than at present, and in places peat accumulated. Fragments of this peat are occasionally to be seen washed up on the beach after storms.

The foundation of Whiteford Point is the mass of glacial deposits left by ice in the Loughor Valley. An exposure of this material may be seen at low tide between the lighthouse (SS 444973) and the tip of the point (SS 447967). This exposure shows signs of frost-cracking patterns. Although subsequently swamped by the rising level of the sea, during the Flandrian transgression, the deposit does not appear to be much disturbed other than in its immediate surface. Some of the stone content has been washed out and partially rounded and now forms part of the foundation of Whiteford Point. Though usually covered by foredunes, these pebbles may be seen after storms have washed the accumulating sand from the upper part of the beach. A recurved shingle bank and subsequent recurved sandbank lie at the northern end of the point, indicating movement of shingle and sand around Whiteford Point when suitable conditions occur.

The drift surface presumably must have had some relief which was gradually swamped and smoothed by the sea. It is interesting to speculate whether Berges Island (SS 450960), now part of the Point, was ever at one time an island isolated by the rising level of the sea, and upon which the accumulating dunes have been driven. The origin of the sand is the same as has been described for other locations – such as Pennard and Oxwich. The sand was brought near to the present coast by the advancing Flandrian shoreline and later (from the Bronze Age until the end of the eighteenth century) re-distributed by the wind.

The sand dune complex of Whiteford Burrows covers the spit and is about 3km long with an average width of between 400m and 600m. The largest dunes occur in the north-east where they attain a height of 24m. These dunes are not completely fixed and change their form appreciably. The main dune ridge is 10m to 16m in height for most of its length, but at the landward end, near Cwm Ivy, it becomes wider with dunes between 12m and 16m high. West of the main dune ridge is a line of dune slacks and a further line of dunes where sand is still actively accumulating. Because they are deeply scoured the slacks have steep sides. East of the main ridge is a second line of dune slacks, larger in size but surrounded by gentler slopes and lower dunes fixed by vegetation. As the dunes rest upon an impervious base of boulder clay, water accumulates during the winter until the low-lying slacks between the dunes are flooded. Those dune slacks which have not been excavated to the water-table remain moist for long periods, and both situations permit a more varied vegetation.

Access

Whiteford Point is a National Nature Reserve to which access is difficult. Before making a visit, especially with a group, advice should be sought from the Countryside Council for Wales (Tel: 01792 771949). The Reserve is approached through the hamlet of Cwm Ivy where there is no car park.

LLANRHIDIAN MARSH

The north Gower coast has a completely different appearance from that of the south coast. Although there is a limestone cliff, it descends from the plateau at about 60m above sea-level into the marshes of the Loughor Estuary. The River Loughor completely crosses the South Wales Coalfield structural basin, but having reached the northern side of the Gower Peninsula, the river then makes an abrupt turn westwards to cross a down-faulted trough of Coal Measures in which the estuary lies. Within the estuary, an unknown thickness of boulder clay is covered by muddy fine sands and silty clays which were probably derived from re-worked glacial drift or outwash material (Figure 18). Interbedded peat and sand layers occur between 3.5m and 5m below the marsh surface and intertidal sandy silts complete the succession.

Development of Llanrhidian Marsh took place naturally until the mid-eighteenth century after which human interference in the course of the River Loughor encouraged scour on the northern side and accretion on the southern side of the estuary. As a result, marshland on the southern side extended at the expense of the sandflats, further encouraged by the introduction of *Spartina anglica* in 1935 which has now replaced *Salicornia* as the primary coloniser. Study of old maps and documents has shown that between 1790 and 1900 the marshes increased by 307ha, and in the following 60 years by 252ha. The highest parts of the marsh have marked stability, as is demonstrated by the similarity of the creek patterns on old Ordnance Survey maps and archival air photographs. However, the lower reaches of the

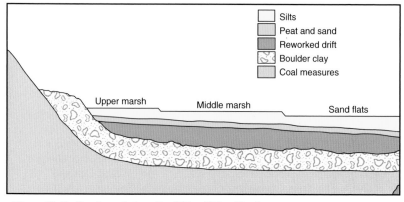

Figure 18: Section through deposits of Llanrhidian Marsh.

creeks show considerable variation where they would be affected by sedimentation and the natural tendency of creeks to meander (Photo 13).

The twice-daily ebb and flow of tides involves large quantities of water which flow in and out of the creeks. When the tides are of sufficient height to cover the marsh interfluves, movement of water is slowed and hindered by the presence of vegetation. In these conditions, sedimentation is encouraged, raising the general level of the marsh. Although the banks of creeks may be undermined by scour, the effects of slumping and frost should not be under-estimated. Slumping of the creek sides can lead to blockage and the development of sinuous pans, flooded at spring tides and dried out at neap tides, producing well-developed cracking patterns. Vegetation has difficulty in establishing upon these pans because of the high salt content left as the water evaporates.

The marsh sediments are unconsolidated and easily eroded. Consequently a delicate balance exists between erosion and sedimentation. Although apparently level, the marsh has a gradient of 1:240 towards the sea interrupted by the presence of small breaks of slope which indicate that the marsh has been built up and subsequently eroded. Where this has occurred in the past it appears that a secondary marsh has developed at a lower level in front of the break of slope which was then preserved. The highest part of the marsh, nearest to the upland (Figure 18), is flooded for a few days a year on the highest spring tides, and because leaching by rainwater is sufficient to remove soluble salts from the soil, the grass *Festuca rubra* is able to colonise.

Photo 13: Part of the Llanrhidian Marsh creek systems. *Photo: EM Bridges.*

The Llanrhidian salt marshes have been allowed to remain in a semi-natural state, being subjected only to grazing pressure by sheep and ponies. Only one small area, Cwm Ivy Marsh, has been embanked and this reclamation took place in 1638. As a result Llanrhidian Marsh is an important site for migratory birds and other birds of the sea shore. Cockles are harvested from the sandflats of the estuary and a local industry is involved in cleaning, boiling and bottling them for the retail market. The shells of cockles have been dumped at several places but the largest accumulation occurs in the former harbour at Pen-clawdd which has been infilled.

The other major glacial feature of the Loughor Estuary is the recessional moraine which can be seen at the village of Crofty (SS 525955). It is a low ridge of glacial debris which protrudes into the estuary and a similar promontory extends towards it from the northern side, known as Penrhyn Gwyn (SS 515973). After depositing the till upon which Whiteford Point is situated, the Loughor glacier front retreated until it was positioned halfway along the present estuary where the accumulation of morainic debris, now partly submerged by the marsh sediments, took place.

CEFN BRYN

Marine platforms or exhumed plains?

It may at first seem strange to climb to the top of one of the higher hills of Gower, to a point far removed from the sea, to discuss coastal evolution. Yet, from the vantage point of Cefn Bryn (SS 495900), either east of Reynoldston (SS 485900) where the minor road between the B4271 and the A4119 crosses the summit, or on the slopes north of Penmaen (SS 532887) it is possible to see the extensive plateau surface of Oxwich Point and other parts of Gower with the same or similar elevation. This surface, approximately 60m above sea-level and cut independently of geological structure, was interpreted by Goskar and Trueman (1934) as a plain of marine abrasion. These authors also identified other strong coincidences of surface level along the coast of South Wales at 130m and 180m. Looking eastward from Cefn Bryn it is possible to see a remnant of the 130m surface on Clyne Common (SS 589908). This is the only evidence in Gower for an erosion surface at this height, but it is extensive elsewhere in South Wales. The higher hills of Gower all have an accordant summit level at approximately 180m; the eastern end of Cefn Bryn attains 186m, The Beacon on Rhossili Down 193m and Llanmadoc Hill 186m.

Observation reveals that these surfaces have a moderate amount of relief and erosion has lowered the 180m surface to 158m where the road from Reynoldston to Cillibion crosses the summit. According to some authorities, development of all landforms in Wales below 215m has resulted from the dissection of coastal plateaus such as the examples seen in Gower. This implies a considerable change in the relationship of land and sea-levels since these surfaces were cut. Although it is theoretically possible to say that these surfaces have a sequence from oldest (highest) to youngest (lowest), it is difficult to say when they were formed. It can be established without doubt that they are pre-glacial and correlations have been attempted with early Pleistocene shorelines in south-east England and even as far away as the Mediterranean Sea. In view of the considerable amount of tectonic disturbance (revealed by the search for oil around the shores of Britain) it is now thought highly unlikely that correlations can be made, certainly not with features as far away as the coast of the Mediterranean Sea.

Another possible explanation for these extensive, almost level surfaces is that they are remains of a buried Triassic desert landscape which has been exhumed by erosion. The development of replacement slopes of very low angle (**pediments**) is a characteristic feature of desert landscapes and the processes involved provide a more plausible explanation for the cutting of these surfaces across the complicated geological structure of Gower than marine processes. Once cut, these surfaces were gradually submerged under desert detritus which preserved their form throughout the Mesozoic until they were again revealed by erosion in the Tertiary. This hypothesis is based on the evidence, near Port-Eynon, of an outcrop of Triassic breccia which was laid down in a pre-existing valley. This is positive evidence that in Triassic times (213-248 MYBP) some of the relief of the area which was to become Gower was already in existence. The presence near Mumbles and Rhossili of red iron-rich deposits in the joints of the limestone has been commented upon; these could be the last remnants of unconsolidated desert deposits of Triassic age, most of which have been stripped from the former desert pediments (Owen and Bridges, 1979).

Pediments at different levels can be seen in desert regions at the present day, simultaneously being cut back into the bedrock. It is an attractive alternative hypothesis for the origin of these surfaces which presents fewer difficulties than are associated with multiple changes of sea-level and the complications of depression of the land by the weight of ice (and rebound as the ice melted) during the glacial episodes of the Pleistocene.

Access
The vantage point described above is marked on Landranger sheet number 159 (SS 495899) by the side of a minor which can be reached from the south via the A4118 or from the north via the B4271. Similar views of the 60m surface can be obtained by walking up the eastern end of Cefn Bryn from Penmaen church (SS 532887).

GLOSSARY

Anglian An early cold stage of the Pleistocene – c. 164-115 000 years BP.

Anticline A structure in sedimentary rocks in which the strata are folded in the form of an arch. In a pitching anticline the axis is not horizontal.

Cave earth Soil material washed into a cave and containing rock fragments split from the roof by frost action, often containing fossil bones.

Devensian The final cold stage of the Pleistocene – from c. 115-10 000 years BP.

Diamicton A non-sorted terrigenous deposit containing a wide range of particle sizes; it excludes sorted beds of sand or silt. Its use avoids using a genetic term for a deposit.

Dune slack A low-lying area between sand dunes where the water table lies just below the surface giving moister conditions and resulting in a more varied plant life. Dune slacks may flood in winter and following heavy rain.

Flandrian transgression The post-glacial rise in sea-level as Pleistocene glaciers melted and flooded low-lying coastal regions – c. 10 000 years BP-present.

Head Deposit of unconsolidated rock material accumulated on slopes under the effect of gravity, usually in a periglacial environment (see solifluction).

Ipswichian Name given to the last major interglacial period – c. 130-118 000 years BP.

Loess Silt-sized material deposited primarily by wind, derived from sediments produced by glacial action.

Marine abrasion platform Extensive coastal plateau surfaces, now elevated above sea-level, were thought to be formed by the action of the sea trimming the rocks to an almost level surface. A greatly extended shore platform.

Pediment An extensive, almost level or slightly sloping plain resulting from the process of back-wearing of mountain slopes, commonly seen in arid and semi-arid regions.

Periglacial An environment typical of regions marginal to glaciers, now confined to high elevations or high latitudes where freeze-thaw processes are dominant.

Piedmont glacier The result of a union of several valley glaciers in amlobate form on an adjacent lowland area.

Raised beach Refers specifically to an accumulation of rounded pebbles, sand and included fossils which may be cemented with calcium carbonate and which normally lies on a shore platform elevated above present sea-level.

Rendzina Dark, organic-rich shallow soil developed upon unconsolidated calcareous materials in areas of chalk and limestone bedrock.

Solifluction The process of rapid mass-movement of thawed, saturated soil and rock material down slopes under the influence of gravity. It is most common in periglacial environments.

Solifluction terrace An extensive accumulation of solifluction debris at the foot of a hillside or cliff.

Syncline A structure in sedimentary rocks in which the strata are folded in the form of a trough or inverted arch.

Talus (Scree) A sloping accumulation of shattered rock material at the foot of a cliff or beneath a rock outcrop.

Till (or **boulder clay**) Terms which describe unconsolidated rock material scraped off the landscape by glacial ice and deposited elsewhere; often a clay containing stones of various sizes and composition.

BIBLIOGRAPHY

Ball, D.F. (1960) 'Relic soil on limestone in South Wales', *Nature (Lond)*, 187, 4736, pp. 497-498.

Bowen, D.Q. (1973) 'Time and place on the British coast', *Geography*, 58, pp. 207-216.

Bowen, D.Q. (1981) 'The South Wales end moraine: fifty years after' in Neale, J. and Flenley, J. (eds) *The Quaternary of Britain*. Oxford: Pergamon.

Bowen, D.Q. and Henry, A. (eds) (1984) *Wales: Gower, Preseli, Fforest Ffawr.* Field Guide Quaternary Research Association.

Bridges, E.M. (1970) 'The shape of Gower', *Gower*, 21, pp. 65-70.

Bridges, E.M. (1985) 'Gower: the Ice Age limit', *Gower*, 36, pp. 71-79.

Bridges, E.M. (1990) 'The physical landscape of Gower' in Humphreys, G. (ed) *Geographical Excursions from Swansea.* Third edition. Swansea: Department of Geography, University College of Swansea.

Campbell, S. and Bowen, D.Q. (1989) *Geological Conservation Review: Quaternary of Wales.* Peterborough: Nature Conservancy Council.

Campbell, S. and Shakesby, R.A. (1994) 'Late Pleistocene deposits at Broughton Bay, Gower, South Wales: evidence for deposition at a non-marine Devensian ice margin', *Proceedings of the Geologists' Association*, 105, pp. 167-185.

Culver, S.J. (1976) 'The development of the Swansea Bay area during the past 20,000 years', *Gower*, 27, pp. 58-62.

George, T.N. (1932) 'The Quaternary beaches of Gower', *Proceedings of the Geologists' Association of London*, 43, pp. 291-324.

George, T.N. (1940) 'The structure of Gower', *Quarterly Journal of the Geological Society of London*, 96, pp. 131-198.

Goskar, K.L. and Trueman, A.E. (1934) 'The coastal plateaux of South Wales' *Geological Magazine*, 71, pp. 468-477.

Harris, C. (1973) 'The Ice Age in Gower as illustrated by coastal landforms and deposits; Heatherslade to Hunt's Bay', *Gower*, 24, pp. 74-79.

Harris, C. (1974) 'Oxwich Burrows', *Gower*, 25, pp. 48-56.

Owen, T.R. and Bridges, E.M. (1979) 'The geological history of Swansea Bay in post-Carboniferous times' in Collins, M.B., Banner, F.T., Tyler, P.A., Wakefield, S.J. and Jones, A.E. (eds) *Industrial Embayments and their Problems.* Oxford: Pergamon.

Owen, T.R. and Rhodes, F.H.T. (1960) *Geology Around the University Towns: Swansea, South Wales.* Benham, Colchester: Geologists' Association Guides No. 17.

Saunders, G.E., Wood, S.J. and Burrin, P.J. (1989) 'Late Glacial and Holocene environmental change in the Gower peninsula, South Wales: evidence from the alluvial valley fill of the Ilston river', *Quaternary Newsletter*, 59, pp. 14-23.

Shakesby, R.A. (1990) 'Quaternary of South Gower' in Humphrys, G. (ed) *Geographical Excursions from Swansea.* 3rd edition. Swansea: Department of Geography, University College of Swansea.

Shakesby, R.A. and Campbell, S. (1985) 'Gower peninsula' in Walsh, R.P.D. and Shakesby R.A. (eds) *Guide to Field Study Excursion in Wales.* Swansea: First International Conference on Geomorphology, Department of Geography, Swansea.

Stringer, C.B. (1977) 'Evidence of climatic change and human occupation during the last interglacial at Bacon Hole, Gower', *Gower*, 28, pp.36-44.

Toft, L. (1988) 'A study of coastal village abandonment in the Swansea Bay region', *Morgannwg*, 32, pp. 21-37.